M000026598

CENTRALIA MIDDLE SCHOOL
901 Johnson Rd.
Centralia, Washington 98531

LONGMAN CLASSICS

Robinson Crusoe

Daniel Defoe

Simplified by D K Swan
and Michael West

Longman

Longman Group UK Limited,
Longman House, Burnt Mill, Harlow,
Essex CM20 2JE, England
and Associated Companies throughout the world.

This simplified edition © Longman Group UK Limited 1987

First published 1987

ISBN 0-582-54156-5

Set in 10/13 point Linotron 202 Versailles
Produced by Longman Group (FE) Limited
Printed in Hong Kong

Acknowledgements

'Photographs © BBC' 1974 for pages 6, 10, 14, 23 and the cover;
Brian Jackson Films Ltd and Sovexportfilm for page 31.

The cover background is a wallpaper design called NUAGE,
courtesy of Osborne and Little plc.

Stage 3: 1300 word vocabulary

Please look under *New words* at the back of this book
for explanations of words outside this stage.

Contents

Introduction

Daniel Defoe

Daniel Defoe (1660–1731) was a journalist. People had become interested in news during the Civil War between Parliament and the king (1642–1646), when it was important to know the latest events. When Charles II came back from Europe in 1660 as king, there was a greatly increased interest in news of happenings, not only in England, but in other countries. News and views about government, right and wrong, truth and values were read by more and more people in newspapers and a growing number of periodicals.

Defoe was a leader in this development of periodicals. In 1704 he started *The Review*. It began as "A review of the affairs of France and of all Europe", and it came out three times a week. Most of the matter in it was written by Defoe himself. He expressed his views on subjects of interest in Britain as well as on the Continent, and this expression of views on political and other matters has led to the development of the "leading article" to be found in most newspapers and periodicals today.

He didn't try to be a writer of "literature". His writing is simple, and he presents the facts (as he sees them) without dressing them up in fine language. That is not to say that he couldn't laugh at his readers: in his *Shortest Way with Dissenters* (1702) he expressed the view that the best thing to do with dissenters (people who did not belong to the

Church of England) was to hang them. In fact, Defoe was himself a dissenter, and his paper was an attack on those who wanted to force people to accept one particular set of beliefs. When the ruling party realised that Defoe was laughing at them, they treated him badly, and he was sent to prison. Public opinion forced the government to set him free after six months.

This factual way of writing, without art, continued when Defoe began to write fiction. *Robinson Crusoe* is a novel, but it was believed at first to be a true account. Defoe seems to have done that on purpose. You read Crusoe's simple statements of fact, like:

> So I cut down a great tree. It was 1.8 metres across at the lower part, and 1.5 metres at the top before it went out into branches. I was twenty days cutting through it at the bottom, and fourteen more days cutting away the branches.

and you think: "This isn't fiction. It's something that really happened."

Alexander Selkirk

Robinson Crusoe wasn't a real person, and Daniel Defoe certainly never was a "castaway" on a "desert island".

But the idea for *Robinson Crusoe* (1719) did come from a true account. In 1704, Alexander Selkirk quarrelled with the captain on the ship on which he was a sailor, Captain William Dampier. Selkirk himself asked to be put off the ship on the island of Juan Fernandez, which at that time had no people on it. He remained there until 1709, when a ship under the command of Captain Rogers, and with Dampier as pilot, found him and took him off the island.

Both captain and pilot were surprised to find him alive.

Defoe added a lot to Selkirk's account, and it was what he added that caught the public imagination and that still makes the story of *Robinson Crusoe* a favourite with young readers.

Robinson Crusoe
What Defoe added was the details – sometimes the very small details:

So I set up a tall thick post, and cut on it in big letters:

I CAME ON SHORE HERE ON MAY 30TH 1659

Each day I cut a small mark on the side of this post. Every seventh mark was larger than the others, meaning a new week. After thirty or thirty-one marks I made a line, meaning a new month.

The result is that people can see everything in their imaginations, and for more than two hundred and fifty years, boys and girls have been playing at being castaways like Robinson Crusoe. Grown-ups, too, have had their imaginations caught. In a British radio programme, well-known people name the records they would like to have with them as castaways on a desert island. It is a very popular programme.

Robinson Crusoe is one of the very few English novels that everybody knows, at least in outline. Crusoe and Friday must be two of the most popular characters in English writing.

Chapter 1
The island

I go to sea

I was born in the year 1632, in the city of York, of a good family. At a very early age I wanted to go to sea. My father was a wise man, and he begged me not to do so. For a time I decided not to think of it any more. But one day in the city of Hull I met a friend who was going to sea on his father's ship. He asked me to go with him. Then, without asking my father, without asking God's blessing, without any thought of the result, I went on board the ship.

The ship is lost in a storm

On the same day we left Hull, meaning to go to the African coast. We guided the ship as if we were going to the island of Fernando de Noronha. Then we passed to the east of that island.

After a few days there came a fearful storm. The wind and the waves threw the ship this way and that for twelve days. The ship was badly broken and a lot of water was coming in. Then one of our men, early in the morning, cried out, "Land!" Just after that, the ship ran on to some sand. The waves came over the ship, and we knew that very soon it would be broken to pieces. We had a small boat on board; we let the boat down into the water, and got into it.

When we had gone some distance in the boat, a great wave came from behind. "Oh, God!" we cried – and we were all thrown into the water.

I am thrown up on the land

A great wave took me and carried me on towards the shore: it left me on the land, badly hurt. I was very weak, but I got up on my feet and ran up to a dry place and lay there more dead than alive. After a time I was sick and threw up a great deal of sea water which had got into my stomach. Then I wanted to rest, but I dared not sleep on the ground for fear of being eaten by wild beasts.

So I climbed up into a tree, and remained there until morning. I was sure that all my friends had been killed and I alone had been saved. I was very tired and I quickly fell asleep.

I go out to the ship

When I woke, it was day. The sea was quiet, and the ship lay less than a kilometre from the shore. I had with me nothing – no food, nor anything with which I might get food. So I decided to go out to the ship to see what useful things I might find there. I took off my clothes and swam to the ship. I climbed through a hole in the side. The lower part was full of water, but the other parts were dry.

Bringing things from the ship

I found four large pieces of board and tied them together to make a raft. Then I put on this raft all the things that I might need from the ship. I took a large box of food, an axe and other things for cutting and shaping wood, seven guns and plenty of powder for the guns, pens and paper, some books, also needles and the few clothes that I could find. I took a small sail and fixed it in my raft. I then sailed towards the shore. When I came near the shore, the front of the raft went up on to the sand, and all my goods began to fall off the end of the raft which was still in the water. I just saved them and held them back. After a lot of hard work I tied the things down, so that my hands were now free to work on the front of the raft and set it back into the water. Then I guided my raft into a little river. There I got all my goods safely on to the land.

I am on an island

My next work was to look at the country, and to find a proper place for a hut to store my goods in and keep them safe. There was a hill not more than two kilometres away. There were other hills, but it seemed to be the highest. I took my gun, and walked to the top of the hill. There I saw with great sadness that I was on an island. The sea was on all sides of me: there was no land to be seen, except two small islands about fourteen kilometres away to the west. I couldn't see any fields or huts on my island, nor anything to show that there were men on it. I saw plenty of birds, but I did not know their kinds, nor which were fit to eat. On my way back I shot at a great bird. I believe that this was the first gun that had ever been fired on the island. At the sound, great numbers of birds of hundreds of sorts flew up, making loud noises of crying and calling.

I make a house to live in

Still looking for a place for my hut, I found a level place on the side of a hill. There was a cave in the side of the hill at the back of this level place, but this cave was small and did not go far into the rock. I brought the sail from my raft, and made a tent on the level ground. Then I drew a half-circle round the tent. In the days that followed, I cut down young trees and made a strong fence round this half-circle. The fence was nearly two metres high, made of posts with sharp points at the top. Then I began to cut away the rock, so as to make the cave larger; and I put the earth and stones inside the fence, so that it raised the ground by about half a metre.

Finishing the house

In this way I had two rooms: my tent in which I would live, and the cave as a store-room. There was no door in the fence, but I made a rough ladder with steps to go over the top, and, when I was in, I lifted the ladder over after me. So I was completely shut in and quite safe.

I then brought all the goods that I had taken from the ship, and put them in my store-room.

After I had been on the island about ten or twelve days, I thought that I should need some way of marking the days. So I set up a tall thick post, and cut on it in big letters:

I CAME ON SHORE HERE ON MAY 30TH 1659

Each day I cut a small mark on the side of this post. Every seventh mark was larger than the others, meaning a new week. After thirty or thirty-one marks I made a line, meaning a new month.

Chapter 2
Making things

Some necessary things

I now began making some things that I needed most. I greatly needed a chair and a table – without them I couldn't write or eat properly. Because I hadn't the proper things for making them, these cost me a great deal of hard work and trouble. For example, when I wanted a board, I had no other way except to cut down a tree, and cut away the round part of the tree on each side with my axe. In this way I could make only one board out of a tree. But I had plenty of time, so I didn't mind.

I made a table and a chair, and I fixed boards all along one side of my store-room; on these I put all my stores and goods in order. Then I had everything ready at hand, and it was a great pleasure to me to see all my goods in order, and to find that I had such a stock of them.

I make a lamp

I didn't know what to do for light in the evening. So, as soon as it was dark, I was forced to go to bed. I might have made a good light with bees' wax, but I had no bees' wax. All I could do was this: whenever I killed and ate any animal, I set the fat on one side. I made a little cup of earth, dried in the sun, which I filled with the fat. With this I made a lamp. This gave me light, though not a clear good light.

Robinson Crusoe in his store-room

Chapter 3
Exploring the island

I find sugar and fruit

I had now been in this unhappy island for more than ten months. Having now made for myself a safe place to live in, I had a great desire to discover more about the rest of the island. I went up the little stream where I had first brought my raft on shore. On the bank of this stream I found grassy plains in which sugar was growing – but wild and not perfect. As I went farther up the stream, these plains ended, and there were more trees. Here I found very many kinds of fruit. I gathered a lot of this fruit because I had thought of a good use for it – that is, to dry it in the sun and keep it with my store of food.

"Home" again

I slept that night in a tree. On the next day I travelled on and came to an opening in the hills, where the country fell away to the west. Here the country appeared so fresh, so green and so full of flowers, that it looked like a planted garden, and I thought with some pleasure that I was king and lord of all this island.

Having spent three days on this journey, I came "home" – as I must now call my tent. I took with me the fruit which I had gathered: but, before I got there, many kinds were bad. I set out the rest to dry in the sun, and after some days I found that they had dried perfectly.

Chapter 4
Making pots and growing corn

The rains

During this month there were heavy rains, so that I could not go out from my tent. For this reason it was not easy to get food.

I did go out twice. The first time, I killed an animal, and on the last day of the rain I caught a large fish. For the rest of the rainy season I ate my dried fruit, and food that I had taken from the ship.

During this time I worked at making my store-room larger. I also made baskets for carrying the earth out of the store-room and to keep food in.

I had no pots (except two very small ones) to hold any liquid. I hadn't a pot in which to boil anything, except one which I had taken from the ship – and that was too big.

I make pots

I looked all over the island, and at last I discovered a kind of clay of which a pot might be made. It would make the reader laugh at me if I told what strange, ugly things I made, how many of the pots fell in, and how many fell out, how many broke and fell to pieces. I worked very hard, but I couldn't make more than two large ugly things – I can't call them "jars" – in about two months' labour. But I made several little pots and cups, and these I was able to make better. I set wood all round the pots that I had made, and kept up a fire outside, and on the top, till the pots were red with the heat. After five or six hours I began to let the fire go down slowly. I watched my pots all night, so that the fire might not go down too quickly. In the morning I had three very good – I won't say "beautiful" – pots, and two jars, all quite strong and useful.

No joy at so little a thing was ever equal to mine, when I found that I had made a pot which would bear the fire. I could not wait till they were cold, but I set one on the fire again with some water to boil some food for me.

I grow some corn

When I first came on the island, I was looking through my things, and I found a little bag. This bag had once held corn for feeding the hens on the ship, but the mice had found the bag, and had eaten a lot of the corn, and had made the rest of it dirty. I wanted to use the bag for something else, so I threw out the grain and dirt from the bag on one side of my house.

It was a little before the great rains when I threw this dirt away, and I hadn't thought about it again. But about a month after that, I saw some green plants growing up out of the ground. After a few more weeks I saw corn forming on the plants. I was greatly surprised, not knowing how it had come there. I went all over that side of the island to see if there was some corn anywhere else, but I found none. Then I remembered cleaning the bag of hen food. I saved that corn, and planted it again as seed. So, saving the grain each time and using it as seed, in time I had a good field of corn, enough to make bread for myself.

Robinson Crusoe explores the island

Chapter 5
The boat

I want a boat

All this time I had been thinking of the islands that I had seen on the other side. I thought that if I could reach those islands, I might find a way of going farther, and perhaps even get home to England again. This made me think whether it was not possible to make a boat for myself – a boat like the ones the Indians make, cut out of a tree. I thought that I might cut out the centre of the tree with my axe, or burn it out with fire, so as to make a boat of it. But I forgot one thing: that I had no one to help me move the boat, when it was made, into the water.

Making a boat

I went to work on this boat more like a fool than any man ever did. I pleased myself with the plan, without ever deciding whether I was able to complete it. The trouble of getting it into the water came into my mind, but I gave myself this foolish answer to the question: "Let me first make the boat; I am sure I shall find some way or other to move it when it is done."

So I cut down a great tree. It was 1.8 metres across at the lower part, and 1.5 metres at the top before it went out into branches. I was twenty days cutting through it at the bottom, and fourteen more days cutting away the branches. After this it took me a month to make it into the shape of a boat outside and three months more to cut out the inside. In the end I had made a very fine boat, big enough to carry ten men – big enough to carry me and all my goods.

I can't get my boat into the water

When I had finished this work, I was delighted with it. I just had to get it into the water. It lay about one hundred metres from the water, but the ground went uphill at first. So I decided to cut through the hill in order to make a road, but, when I had done that, things were no better: I couldn't move the boat at all.

Then I decided to bring the water up to the boat, since I couldn't take the boat to the water.

So I began this work. But when I began to make plans and thought how deep a hole I must make, and how broad, and how much earth must be thrown out, I found that it must be ten or twelve years before I could finish it. So at last, though with great sadness, I gave up the work.

Chapter 6
The mark of a man's foot!

I am afraid

It happened one day about noon after I had been on the island for several years. I was going along the shore, and I was greatly surprised to see the mark of a man's foot in the sand. I stood there like one who has seen a giant or some fearful thing. I listened; I looked round me: I couldn't hear anything or see anything. I went up the shore and down the shore, but I could see no mark except that one. I went to it again to see if it mightn't be a dream, but there it was, the perfect mark of every part of a foot. I couldn't think how it came there.

I went home to my tent looking behind me at every two or three steps, thinking that every plant and tree at a distance was a man.

I make my house stronger

I didn't sleep that night. In the morning I got up out of my bed. "Can it be the mark of my own foot?" I wondered. I went to the shore again, but, when I came to measure the mark with my own foot, I found that my foot wasn't nearly so big.

I went back and made the fence of my home stronger. Then I made seven holes in it, so that I could put out all my guns at one time. I fixed the guns all ready pointed so that I could fire all the seven guns in two minutes. Fear made me do all this, and the mark of a man's foot: I had never seen any man come near the island.

Robinson Crusoe makes his fence stronger

Chapter 7
Cannibals!

I see a boat

One day, when I had wandered more to the west part of the island than I had ever done yet, I thought I saw a boat on the sea at a great distance. But it was so far that I wasn't sure whether it was a boat or not. As I came down from the hill, I couldn't see it any more. I told myself that seeing the print of a man's foot was not such a strange thing in the island as I had thought. It must be common for boats from the other islands, when they were too far out at sea, to come over to this west side of the island to be safe from bad weather. I thought, too, that the wild men of these islands must often meet and fight in their boats, and those who had taken any prisoners might bring them over to this shore, to kill and eat them. Because the wild men of this part of the world do that: they are cannibals.

Dead men's bones

When I came down the hill to the shore at the south-west point of the island, I saw a fearful sight. It's not possible for me to find words for the fear and sickness of my mind at seeing the shore covered with heads, hands, feet, and bones from other parts of men's bodies. I noticed also a place where a fire had been made and a circle had been cut in the earth where, I supposed, these fearful cannibals sat down to feed upon the bodies of their fellow-men.

I was so much surprised by the sight of these things that I had no thought of any danger to myself from it for a long time. I could think only of the condition to which Man can fall. I turned my face away from the sight. My stomach grew sick, and I almost fell to the ground. I couldn't stay in the place one minute. So I went up the hill again as fast as I could, and walked on towards my own house.

I keep watch

On the next day I found a place on the side of the hill where I could safely wait till I saw any of their boats coming. I could then, unseen, go among some trees where I could sit and see all that they did, and point my gun at their heads. I was so near that, if I fired when they were standing close together, I should hit three or four of them at one shot.

Every morning for many days I went to this place on the hill. But I grew tired of this duty after I had kept watch for two or three months and seen nothing; so I stopped going.

It was now the season for gathering in my corn. For this reason I had to go out very early into the field. One morning, going out before it was full daylight, I was surprised to see the light of a fire on the shore: it was about four kilometres away towards the end of the island. I went quickly up the hill, and began to look for the place.

A fearful thing

When I came to this place I saw that there were nine men. They were sitting round a small fire that they had made. They hadn't made the fire to warm them, because the weather was very hot, but – as I supposed – to cook some of their fearful food: their fellow-men. They began dancing: I could see their legs and arms moving. They had no clothes, no covering of any sort on them. After an hour or more they got into their boats, and began to go away.

I ran back to my house to get my gun. When I came back I saw their three boats all at sea together. Going

16

down to the shore, I saw the marks which they had left behind them – the blood and bones of men eaten by these cannibals with joy and laughing. I was so angry at the sight that I began to think how I could kill the next party I saw there, however many they might be.

Chapter 8
The cannibals come again

Five boats

A few years passed, and I saw no more of them. Then one morning I was surprised to see five boats all on shore together on my side of the island. The men had all gone away from the boats, and were out of my sight. But I knew that they always came four or six in a boat: so I knew that there must be twenty or thirty men. I set the guns ready at my house and made everything safe. Then I went up to the top of the hill. From here I could see that there were thirty men, and they had a fire burning. Their food was being made ready, and they were dancing round the fire.

As I looked, I saw two poor fellows pulled from the boat: they were being brought to be killed. I saw a man strike one of them with a wooden axe. The other was left standing by himself until they were ready for him. Just then this poor fellow, finding himself free, started to run away along the sands, coming straight towards me.

A prisoner runs away

I was very much afraid when I saw him run my way, and even more afraid when I saw the whole party following him. But I didn't move, and I began to feel more hope when I saw that only three men continued to follow him.

Between them and me there was the little stream to which I first came with my goods from the ship, and I saw clearly that the poor fellow must cross that stream, or be caught there. The runaway reached the stream, jumped into the water and swam across as easily as a fish. Then he ran on with great strength and quickness. When the three men came to the stream, two of them went into the water; the third didn't, but stopped there, and soon after went quietly back.

I save a man from death

The other two were not good swimmers. They came over the stream very slowly. I saw now that I could save this poor fellow's life. I took my gun, and came quickly down the hill, so as to be between the man escaping and those following. I then shouted to the escaper, and waved my hand to him, to make him come back. Then I slowly went forward towards the two that followed. I ran at the first and struck him on the head with my gun. I didn't want to fire my gun, because the rest of the men might hear. But the other man came towards me so quickly that I was forced to shoot: my first shot killed him. The poor fellow who was escaping saw both his enemies killed, but he was so frightened by the fire and noise of my gun that he stood there, and neither came forward nor went back.

19

Chapter 9
Friday

The man who was saved

I shouted to the poor fellow whom I had saved. He came forward a little way, then stopped; and then came a little farther, and stopped again. I could see that he thought that he was a prisoner again, and was coming to be killed, as his two enemies had been killed. I tried to show him that I was his friend. At last he came close to me, and then he fell on his knees and kissed the ground. Then he put his head on the ground, took my foot, and set it on his head. This, as it seems, was a way of promising to be my servant for ever.

We hide the bodies

What surprised the fellow was to know that I had killed a man so far off. He pointed to him and spoke some words to me. I couldn't understand the words, but I was very glad to hear them: it was the first sound of a man's voice that I had heard in all the years that I had been on the island. He seemed to be saying that he wanted to go and see the man that was killed. I told him to go. When he came to him, he stood looking at him: then he turned him first on one side, then on the other. He looked at the hole that the gunshot had made. Then he made a hole in the sand and put into it the two bodies, so that they wouldn't be seen by the rest if they followed. After that, he followed me to my tent.

My life with Friday begins

When the man came to my tent, I saw that his escape had made him very tired. I gave him bread, some dried fruit, and a cup of water. After that, I made him lie down and sleep.

When he had slept for about half an hour, he woke and came out of the house to me. Then I began to speak to him and to teach him to speak to me. First, I told him that his name would be Friday, because that was the day on which I saved his life. I taught him to say "Master", and then let him know that this was to be my name. I taught him to say "Yes" and "No" and to know the meaning of them.

I gave Friday some trousers and a coat made of animal skins. He was very well pleased to see himself in such clothes. It is true that he moved strangely in the clothes at first: he had never worn clothes before. The coat rubbed his neck and the inside of his arms; but I made it larger, and after that he wore the clothes quite easily.

Friday in my home

On the next day I began to think of a place for him to sleep in. I made him a tent on an open place inside my fence. Then I made a door to my store-room. At night I slept in the store-room. I took with me all my guns, and I shut the door.

I need not have taken all this care: a man never had a more true and loving servant than my Friday. He was never angry. He wanted only to please me. He loved me as a child loves his father, and I think he would have given his life to save mine at any time.

He treated my gun as if it were some sort of god. He never touched it, but he spoke to it when he was alone with it, and he talked to it as if it had answered him. I asked him later what it was that he said to the gun, and he told me that he asked it not to kill him.

Friday learns English

This was the best year of all that I spent on the island. Friday began to talk well, and to understand the names of everything I called for, and of every place I sent him to. He also talked a great deal to me. So I began to have some use for my tongue again: I had hardly used it before for speaking. Besides the pleasure of talking to him, I had great pleasure in the fellow himself. His simple goodness appeared to me more and more every day, and I began to like him very much, and, on his side, I believe that he loved me more than it was possible for him ever to love anything before.

Friday learns English

Chapter 10
Friday's father

Other men come to the island

And so the years passed. I was busy one morning with my stores, and I called to Friday and told him to go to the sea shore, and see if he could get some fish. Friday hadn't been long gone when he came running back. He came flying up the ladder over the wall and, before I had time to speak to him, he cried out to me, "Oh, master! Oh, master! Oh, bad! bad!"

"What has happened, Friday?"

"Oh – there," he said; "one, two, three boats! One, two, three!"

"You mustn't be afraid, Friday," I said. But I saw that the poor fellow was still very much afraid; he often dreamt that they would come to look for him, and that they would cut him in pieces and eat him. I told him that I was in danger too, and that they would eat me as well as him. "But," I said, "we must decide to fight them. Can you fight, Friday?"

"Me – yes – shoot," he said, "but there are many – a great number."

We go to fight against the cannibals

"Don't trouble about that," I said again. "Our guns will make them afraid even if we don't kill them." So I asked him, "Will you stand by me and do just as I order you?"

He said, "I die when you order me to die, master." Then I made ready five guns.

When I had made all my preparations, I went up the

side of the hill to see what I could discover. I found that there were twenty-one men, three prisoners, and three boats, and their business seemed to be to eat their prisoners, as was usual with them.

This sight made me very angry. I gave Friday two of the guns, and took the other three myself. I also gave Friday a large bag with more powder for the guns. I told him to keep close behind me, and not to move or shoot or do anything until I gave the order.

I then went about two kilometres round so as to get among the trees and come close to them without their seeing me.

Sight of the cannibals

I moved among the trees very carefully and silently, Friday following close behind me. I went on till I came to the edge of the trees on the side which was nearest to them. Only one corner of the little forest lay between me and them. Here I called quietly to Friday. I showed him a great tree which was just at the corner of the forest. I told him to go to that tree, and to come back and tell me if he could see what they were doing. He did so, and came back to me at once. He said that they were sitting round the fire eating one of the prisoners, and another prisoner lay tied up on the sand a little distance from them.

There was another tree about forty metres nearer to them. I saw that, by going a little way round, I could reach it without being seen, and then I should be quite close to them. Going back about twenty metres, I got behind some small bushes which continued all the way till I came to the other tree. This gave me a full sight of the cannibals at a very short distance.

25

"Fire at them"

There was not a minute to lose. Seventeen of these fearful cannibals were sitting on the ground all close together, and they had just sent the other four to kill the poor prisoner. They got down on their knees to untie the ropes at the man's feet.

I turned to Friday. "Now, Friday," I said, "do exactly what you see me do."

I put two of my guns on the ground, and Friday put one of his down. Then I took the other gun and pointed it at the cannibals. I asked Friday if he was ready; he said, "Yes."

"Then fire at them," I said, and I fired too.

Friday's shot was better than mine: he killed two of them, and wounded three more. I killed one and wounded two.

We fire again

The result was complete surprise! All of them who were not hurt jumped to their feet, but they didn't know which way to run, or which way to look. Friday kept his eyes on me, so that he could see what I did. As soon as the first shot had been fired, I threw down that gun, and took up my second gun, and Friday did the same. I pointed the gun, and he did the same again.

"Are you ready, Friday?" I said.

"Yes," he said.

"Fire, then!" I fired again, and so did Friday. Only two fell, but many were wounded and ran about shouting, and three more of them fell soon after.

Out from the trees

"Now, Friday," I said, "load your guns and follow me." loaded the guns that I had fired. Then I came out from the trees and showed myself. Friday was close behind me.

As soon as they saw me, I shouted as loud as I could. Then I ran to the place where the poor prisoner lay on the shore. The four men had left him when they were surprised by our first shots. They had got into one of the three boats. I turned to Friday and told him to step forward and fire at the men in the boat. He ran forward till he was fifteen metres from them, then he shot at them. I thought he had killed them all, but one got up again after.

Friday's father

While my man Friday fired at them, I cut the ropes of the poor prisoner, and set free his hands and feet. He couldn't stand or speak, but cried out as if he had been set free only to be killed. I told Friday to speak to him, and tell him that he was saved. But when Friday came to look in the man's face, he kissed him, and cried, and laughed, jumped about, danced, sang; then cried again. It was a long time before I could make him speak to me or tell me the reason. But at last he told me that it was his father.

.Then he ran and brought his father water and bread.

After some days Friday went to take his father back to his home in one of the boats which the men had left.

I didn't expect to see Friday again. I thought he would stay with his own people. But he came back because he had promised to be my man.

Chapter 11
Men on the island

A ship

The years passed.

I was asleep in my house one morning, when Friday came running in to me and called loudly, "Master, master, they have come."

I jumped up and went out as soon as I could get my clothes on. I didn't expect any danger, so I didn't take my gun. But I was surprised when I turned my eyes to the sea and saw a boat about a kilometre away, coming in to the shore. It had a sail, and the wind was blowing well to bring it to the land.

I told Friday to hide, while I went up the hill. From the top of the hill, I saw a ship about a kilometre away on the south side of the island. It seemed to be an English ship, and the boat was the ship's boat.

Men from the ship

I can't find words to say what I felt: I was so delighted at seeing a ship, an English ship! And yet there was some doubt in my mind, telling me to be careful. I wondered why an English ship was in that part of the world, since the island was not on the way to or from any place where the English had any trade, and I knew there had been no storm to drive them there. If they were really English, they could not have come here for any good.

As I lay watching, I saw the boat draw near to the shore. They came to land about a kilometre from me. They were English. There were eleven men, and three of them seemed to have their hands tied, as if they were prisoners.

Four or five of the men jumped out on the shore. Then they took the three prisoners out of the boat.

The ship's boat on the shore

I was most surprised, and couldn't think what the meaning of it could be.

Friday called out to me, "Oh, master! You see, English men eat prisoners too."

"No, no," I said. "I am afraid they may kill them, indeed, but you may be sure they will not eat them."

The men stood talking to the prisoners for a long time, and at every minute I expected to see the three prisoners killed.

But a chance saved them. These men had come to the island when the water was high on the shore. But, while they stood talking to the prisoners, the sea went down, leaving their boat dry on the shore. They had left two men in the boat, but these men had fallen asleep. One of them woke and saw what had happened. He called to the others, and they came quickly to the boat, but they couldn't move it. Then they all went away, deciding to wait for the next high water.

The three prisoners

They went up the shore as if they wanted to see the inside part of the island.

I went to my house and made everything ready for a battle as before. Then I decided to show myself to the three prisoners, and find out something about them.

I came as near to them as I could without being seen. Then I called out to them, "Who are you, gentlemen?"

They jumped up in surprise, but they were ten times more surprised when they saw me, because indeed I must

29

have looked very strange in the clothes that I had made for myself on the island. They made no answer.

"Gentlemen," I said again, "don't be surprised at me; perhaps you may have a friend near you when you didn't expect it."

"The friend must be sent from heaven, then," said one of them sadly, "because no man can do anything to help us."

"I'm an Englishman," I said, "and I want to help you. I have one servant only, but we have guns and powder. Tell me freely: can we help you? What has happened to you?"

"I was the captain of that ship," replied one of the prisoners. "My men rose up against me. At one time they meant to kill me, but now they have set me on shore in this unknown place, and these two men with me. One of these men is my officer, and the other is a passenger on the ship."

"Have they any guns?" I asked. He answered that they had only two guns and one which they had left in the boat – that is, three in all.

We find five men

It was now the hottest part of the day. Going a little forward, I saw the five men were all asleep among some trees not very far from where we stood. The three others were still walking somewhere in the island.

I came back and said to the captain, "Here are three guns for you and your party." I asked him whether we should fire on the five sleeping men, but the captain said that only two of the men were bad, and they ruled the others through fear.

While we were speaking, we heard some of the men waking up, and soon after we saw two of them standing

The men and their prisoners on the shore

up. I asked the captain if these were the two leaders. He said, "No."

"Then," I said, "you may let them escape, and God seems to have awakened them so that they may save themselves. Now," I said, "don't let the rest escape you."

Then we all took our guns. The two men who were with the captain went first. They made some noise, so that one of the men woke up and saw them coming. He cried out to the rest, but it was too late: as he cried out, the officer and the other man fired. One man was killed, and one, who was wounded, cried out, "Help!" At that another man jumped up. The captain stepped forward and hit him on the head with the heavy part of his gun, so that he never spoke again. The man who was wounded died soon after.

I tell the captain my story

By this time I had arrived. When the two others saw their danger, and knew that they could do nothing, they begged the captain not to kill them. The captain told them that he would give them their lives if they promised to help him in getting his ship again. They gave the promise, but we tied their hands and feet. While this was being done, I sent Friday with the officer to the boat to take it.

The three men who had not been with the others came back when they heard the guns. Seeing what had happened, they also promised to serve the captain, and we tied them up and left them with the others.

So we had won everything.

I told the captain my story. He was most surprised at it, and was delighted at hearing the wonderful way in which I had got stores and powder and guns, and, when he thought how God seemed to have kept me safe on the island so that I might save his life, the tears ran down his face, and he couldn't speak another word.

After this I led him and the two men to my house. I gave them some of my island food, and showed them my table and chair and pots, and other things that I had made during my long years in the place.

Chapter 12
The end of the fight

Another boat comes from the ship

We then began to think how we could take the ship. The captain said that there were still twenty-six men on board. We didn't know how we could fight so many.

Then the thought came to me that the men on the ship would wonder what had happened to the eleven men who had come in the boat, and would ask why they hadn't returned. And then they would come on shore in another boat to look for them. So we must make a hole in the boat which was now on the shore, so that they couldn't take it away.

Just as we finished doing this, we heard the ship fire a gun; then we saw a flag go up, as an order to the others to return. But no boat came. They fired another gun, and put up other flags.

At last they put out a boat with ten men in it, and it came towards the shore. As the ten men came near, the captain saw them, and said that three of them were very good fellows who had been led by fear of the others: the other seven were bad.

They pulled their boat up on the sand, then they all ran to their other boat. It was easy to see that they were surprised to see the great hole in it.

Then they shouted to try to make the others hear, but there was no answer. Then they all came close in a ring, and fired off their guns together. Our prisoners heard it, but they dared not give any answer.

Friday and the officer lead the men away
The leader told two men to stay with the boat, and the other eight came marching towards the top of the little hill under which my house lay. I ordered Friday and the officer to go to the little stream on the west and as soon as they came to high ground, to shout. When the men from the ship answered, they must shout again; then, keeping out of sight, they must draw the men on far into the island among the trees.

When the men from the ship heard Friday and the officer shouting, they ran along the shore towards the sound. As soon as they had gone into the island, we came down and surprised the two men who were with the boat, and made them prisoners. Then we moved the boat away and hid it. They were two good fellows, and they were very ready to work for us. So we let them keep their guns.

During this time, Friday and the officer did their work very well. By shouting and answering they drew the others from one hill to another till they were very tired and did not know where they were. Indeed Friday and the officer were themselves very tired when they came back to us.

The seven men came back several hours later. Long before they came near, we could hear the men in front calling to those behind to come along, and the men behind answering how tired they were, and not able to come any faster.

It was growing dark by that time.

I fight against seven men
At last the seven men came to the place where their boat had been. Their surprise was very great when they found

35

the boat gone and the two men gone too. We could hear them call to one another that they had got on to an island of fairies or magic, and that they would all be carried away.

I ordered Friday and the captain to go on their hands and knees as close to the ground as they could, and get as near to them as possible.

After a little time the leader of these fellows came walking towards them with two others. As they came near, Friday and the captain jumped up, and shot at them. The leader was killed; another was wounded and died soon after; and the third ran away.

The men lay down their guns

I at once came forward with all my army, which was now eight men. I ordered one of the men who had been guarding the boat to speak to them. So he called out, "Tom Smith, Tom Smith."

Tom Smith answered, "Who is that? Is it Jones?" – because he knew the voice.

Our man answered, "Throw down your guns, Tom Smith, or you are all dead men this minute."

"Who are they?" said Smith again.

"Our captain and forty men with him," said the other. "They have been following you for two hours. Your leader is killed; Will Frye is wounded, and I am a prisoner."

"Will we be safe?" said Smith.

Then the captain himself called out, "You, Smith, you know my voice. If you put down your guns at once, you shall have your lives."

Then they laid down their guns, and I sent two men to tie their hands and feet.

Taking the ship

Then we stopped the hole in the boat, and the captain went off with his officer and four other men to the ship.

There were two men on guard at the side of the ship. It was quite dark, but they heard the boat coming. The captain made Jones shout to them, and say they had brought away the men and the boat from the island. While this was being said, they came to the side of the ship. The captain and the officer climbed up quickly, and made the two men prisoners. Then they shut the openings which led to the lower part of the ship, and made all the other sailors prisoners. Their leader was in another part of the ship. The officer broke the door of the room where he was, and, running in, shot him through the head. Then the other men gave in, and the ship was taken.

The captain ordered seven guns to be fired, so that I might know that the ship was taken. I was very glad, and lay down to sleep.

I awoke to hear the sound of a gun, and soon after that I heard the captain's voice. I climbed up to the top of the hill. There the captain stood. Pointing to the ship, he said, "My friend, you have saved me, and there is *your* ship. The ship is all yours, and so are we, and all that is in the ship."

Home at last!

I offered to take Friday to his own island, but he begged me to take him with me. I took him and I also took some of the things that I had made, so that I might remember the island in after-years. I left the island in 1687, after I had been on it twenty-eight years, two months and seventeen days.

I made many other journeys and travelled to many

other lands. There is no time now to write about them. I am an old man now. I am preparing for a longer journey than any of these. I have lived many years, a life of many changes, and I have learned the blessing of ending our days in peace.

Questions

Questions on each chapter

1 The island
1. Where did Robinson Crusoe sail from?
2. Where did they want to sail to?
3. When did the ship run on to the shore?
4. Why did Crusoe climb a tree? (Because . . .)
5. How did he reach the ship? (He . . .)
6. What did Crusoe use to make a tent?
7. There was no door in the fence, so how did Crusoe get in and out?

2 Making things
1. Where did he put his stores?
2. What did he burn in his lamp?

3 Exploring the island
1. Why did he go up the stream? (To . . .)
2. How did he keep his fruit from going bad?

4 Making pots and growing corn
1. Why did Crusoe need pots, besides the one he had taken from the ship?
2. What did he find to make pots from?
3. What grew where Crusoe had emptied a bag?

5 The boat
1. What did Crusoe make from a big tree?
2. What mistake did he make?

6 The mark of a man's foot!
1. Where was the footmark?
2. Why did Crusoe make holes in his fence? (So that . . .)

7 *Cannibals!*
1 What did Crusoe think he saw at a distance?
2 What did he do when he had seen the men's bones?
3 Why did he go out very early one morning?
4 What did he want to do to the cannibals?

8 *The cannibals come again*
1 How many cannibals came to Crusoe's island?
2 Which way did the escaping man run?
3 How did Crusoe kill the second cannibal?

9 *Friday*
1 How did the runaway show that he promised to be Crusoe's servant?
2 How did the runaway hide the bodies of the cannibals?
3 Why was the man's name to be Friday? (Because . . .)
4 Where did Crusoe sleep?
5 What did Friday say to Crusoe's gun?

10 *Friday's father*
1 What did Friday see?
2 What had the cannibals come to do?
3 In what way was Friday more successful than Crusoe with a gun?
4 Who was the prisoner they saved?
5 Why did Friday go away?
6 Why did he return to Crusoe?

11 *Men on the island*
1 How far from the island was the ship?
2 Who had their hands tied?
3 What happened while the men were talking to the prisoners?
4 Who were the prisoners?
5 How many men were asleep?
6 What happened to them?

12 *The end of the fight*
1 How many men were still on the ship?
2 What did Crusoe and his friends do to the first boat from the ship?
3 What did Crusoe and his friends do with the second boat?

4 How big was Crusoe's "army"?
5 How many men did Jones say were with the captain?
6 How did Crusoe know that the ship was taken?
7 Why didn't Crusoe take Friday to his own island?

Questions on the whole story

These are harder questions. Read the Introduction, and think
hard about the questions before you answer them. Some of them
ask for your opinion, and there is no fixed answer.

1 Was Crusoe a brave man? Can you give two examples to
  support your answer?

2 Was he a religious man? Give examples to support your
  answer.

3 Make a list of the things Crusoe brought from the ship. Then
  add the use he made of them. Here is an example:

Things brought from the ship	Use
1. An axe	To cut wood. To make a fence.

4 Make a list of things he made for himself. Add the use he made
  of them.

Things made on the island	Use
1. A ladder	To climb over the fence.

5 In your opinion, how well did he treat Friday?

6 How many years did Crusoe spend on the island? Compare this
  with the time Alexander Selkirk spent alone on the island of
  Juan Fernandez (see the Introduction).

7 At the end of the story Robinson Crusoe says: "I am preparing
  for a longer journey than any of these." What does he mean?

New words

cannibal
a person who eats the meat of men and women

clay
soft, sticky earth

fellow
another word for a man

fiction
stories about things that didn't really happen

fire (a gun)
shoot

journalist
a writer for newspapers and periodicals (papers that come out once a week, month, etc)

level
not sloping; not with one part higher than another

novel
a long story with invented people and happenings, printed as a book

raft
large pieces of wood joined together to make a rough flat boat

views
opinions, thoughts about the news and ideas, etc